# *Wildflowers*

## Western **of** Australia

Simon Nevill   Gift Book Series

# Wildflowers

## Western of Australia

**There is nowhere in Australia that displays a greater abundance of wildflowers than South Western Australia, particularly in spring time.**

In an overpopulated world with mass land clearing still taking place, many of us are turning to the natural world to gain pleasure and solace. To see the carpets of everlastings or the amazing variety of species in the heath lands of the south west is a real pleasure. This small book attempts to show the diversity and beauty of the major plant families to be found in Western Australia.

Over millions of years, the earth's massive crustal plates have moved with the passing of time. As a result the position of the continents have changed and there is significant evidence that during the Jurassic period (more than 135 million years ago) there existed a massive great southern continent called Gondwanaland when South America, Africa, Antartica and Australia were linked. During the period when these continents split from each other, the present day plant families were established such as the Proteaceae family, now represented in South Africa by such wonderful flowers as the Protea and here in Australia by the beautiful Banksia, Dryandra, Hakea, Grevillea, etc.

Looking at a map of Western Australia will show you that now there are seas to west and south and deserts and dry country to the north and east of the south west botanic province. This has proved to be a major barrier to the movement of plant specie from outside this region. Also there has been virtually no major changes in the habitats over the last few thousand years and plants have reached a state of development quite different to other regions of the world. As a result the south west alone possesses one of the richest floras in the world with over 9000 species.

# The major plant families of Western Australia

Within this book you will find listed some of the major plant families of Western Australia and contained in these family groups are illustrated some of the representative genera and species (the meaning of these botanical terms are mentioned below).

Whereever possible the common name as well as the true scientific name has been given, as for the beginner they are often easier to remember.

Some family groups have many species such as the family Myrtaceae which contain the world renowned genus, Eucalyptus, commonly called Gum Trees, of which there are over 500 species. A book of this size can only represent a small sample of species within each genus but it will give you an idea of the shape and structure of some of the typical plants in each group.

Family titles are orange. Genus titles are green.

# How plants are named

In the plant world, there are universally accepted categories established by botanists on how plants are related to one another. This is represented in the diagram illustrated right. This covers the level from family category to the species level. The individual scientific name that is given to each unique plant found on this planet is represented by a two word name based on either Latin or Greek. This is called the binominal system. So for example the gum tree with the common name 'Jarrah' found in the south west has two names; Eucalyptus marginata. The first is the Genus name and the second is the species name.

The use of common names is convenient when you first start to look at plants but soon it shows its limitations as there are often no common name for a given plant, or worse still, people have given it several common names, but we have attempted to list both the common and the scientific name where possible.

## Typical Family Tree

**Family** (example the Myrtles–Scientific name *Myrtaceae*)
A family comprised of one or more genera that share the same fundamental characteristics.

**Genus** (example the Gum Trees–Scientific name *Eucalyptus*)
Genus contain one or more species that share the same characteristics.

**Species** (example the gum tree called Jarrah–Scientific name *Eucalyptus marginata*)
An individual plant that possesses specific characteristics that make it unique from any other plant.

*Banksia menziesii* Firewood Banksia

# Proteaceae
## proteas

Named after the plant genus Protea of South Africa by Carl Linnaeus in 1735. He was so astounded at the great variation in shape and colour within this family group that he named it after the Greek sea-god Proteus who could change his shape at will.

The Proteaceae is the most extensive southern hemisphere plant family with 75 genera and more than 1800 species, with the greatest diversity in Australia, 45 genera and 860 species, the largest number occuring here in the south west. South Africa has 14 genera and 330 species.

Proteaceae plants usually grow on infertile sandy soils or laterite gravels and can vary from tall trees to prostrate shrubs. They are an ancient plant group and even though there is great variation in shape and colour between the various genera, they all share a distinctive floral structure.

# Dryandra

Named after the Swedish botanist Jonas Dryander (1748–1810). Dryander succeeded the other Swede Daniel Solander as the librarian to the famous English botanist Sir Joseph Banks. The first plants were collected by the English botanist Robert Brown in 1801 from King George Sound on the south coast.

Most species are referred to by their genus name but some of the prostrate plants are known as Honeypots because of the copious amount of nectar that is produced by them. The genus is totally restricted to the south west, reaching its greatest density in two areas; the Stirling Range and the Eneabba area. The leaves are often prickly and form thick dense stands of bushes, making progress difficult when walking.

*Dryandra cuneata* Wedge-leaved Dryandra

*Dryandra formosa* Showy Dryandra

*Dryandra speciosa* Shaggy Dryandra

*Banksia coccinea* Scarlet Banksia

*Banksia speciosa* Showy Banksia

*Banksia burdettii* Burdett's Banksia

*Banksia praemorsa* Cutleaf Banksi

# Banksia

Named after Sir Joseph Banks who collected the first specimens of this genus during the journeys on Captain Cook's ship Endeavour in 1770. It was however the English botanist Robert Brown who in 1802 found many of the south west's Banksias, 13 in all. In latter years Charles Gardner named 6 new species and finely the eminent botanist Alex George named a further 11 species with additional sub species.

Banksias normally have thick and deeply dissected leaves and are woody, evergreen plants varying from tall trees to small prostrate plants. Some species have fire tolerant trunks while others are killed by fire but regenerate from seed. Looking at the wonderful plants on this page it is not hard to understand why they are extremely popular in the cut flower trade.

*Banksia sceptrum* Sceptre Banksia

*Banksia nutans var. cernuella* Nodding Banksia

# Adenanthos
## Woollybushes or Jugflowers

Named from the Greek 'aden' meaning gland and 'anthos' meaning flower. This refers to the prominent nectaries within the floral tube.

The genus is restricted to Australia, there being 34 species with only 2 occuring outside Western Australia. They are normally recognized by their red flowers with long styles.

*Adenanthos barbigerus* Hairy Jugflower

*Adenanthos cuneatus* Coastal Jugflower

*Adenanthos obovatus* Basket Flower

# Conospernum
## Smokebushes

From the Greek 'Konos' a cone and 'sperma' a seed referring to the seed shape and the common name to the smoke like appearance that some species have when seen at a distance.

There are 36 species with 29 here in Western Australia. The genus normally grows in well drained soils, often forming the dominant plant understorey.

They are used quite extensively in the cut flower trade.

*Conospermum brachyphyllum* Smokebush

*Conospermum brownii* Blue eyed Smokebush

# Grevilleas

*Grevillea insignis sub.sp insignis*
Wax Grevillea

Named after Charles Francis Greville (1749–1809) one of the founders of the Royal Horticultural Society of Britain and Vice Chancellor to King George III. Grevilleas are found in most habitats in Australia including rainforest; but here in the south west they are mostly found in Laterite or sandy soils.

Grevilleas, like Banksias, range from tall trees to prostrate plants and their leaf structure varies enormously but they are easily recognized by their shell like fruit which falls in the same season. They are widely cultivated throughout the world.

The genus is almost totally endemic to Australia with a few species found in Malaysia, New Guinea and New Caledonia, but over half the species can be found here in the south west.

*Grevillea excelsior* Flame Grevillea

*Grevillea wilsonii* Wilsons Grevillea

*Grevillea paradoxa* Bottlebrush Grevillea

*Grevillea bipinnatifida* Fuchsia Grevillea

13

# Isopogon

From the Greek 'isos' meaning equal and 'pogon' meaning a beard referring to the hairs that surround the nut seed on all sides. There are 34 species with 25 in the south west.

*Isopogon teretifolius* Nodding Coneflower

*Isopogon sphaerocephalus* Drunstick Isopogon

*Isopogon cuneatus* Coneflower

# Lambertia
## *Honeysuckles*

Named in honor of the English botanist Aylmer Bourke Lamberts. There are 11 species with all but one confined to the south west some of them being quite rare and restricted to small areas. Most flower colours range from yellow, orange to bright red.

*Lambetia propinqua* A Honeysuckle

*Lambetia ericfolia* Heath-leaved Honeysuckle

*Lambetia inermis* Chittick

# Hakea

Named in honour of the German patron of botany Baron Christian Ludwig von Hake (1745–1818) by the German botanist Henrich Schrader.

There are over 130 species in Australia, all endemic to this country. The flowers are similar to Grevilleas, but the fruits are often different. They are very hard and woody and often quite large, typically not opening until the plant or branch dies. The leaves quite prickly.

*Hakea laurina* Emu Bush

*Hakea petiolaris* Sea-urchin Hakea

*Hakea conchifolia* Shell-leaved Hakea

*Hakea bucculenta* Red Pokers

*Hakea pandanicarpa*

*Hakea Victoria* Royal Hakea

*Hakea cucullata* Hood-leaved Hakea

# Synaphea

There is no common name for this genus. The species are normally low to prostrate plants occurring in sandy or gravelly soil in heath or woodland and always have yellow flowers, and most have dissected leaves.

*Synaphea flabellifomis* A Synaphea

# Persoonia

Named in honour of Christian Hendrik Persoon, the South African Botanist. The genus is currently under review and to determine the number of species is difficult but there are at least 14 in Western Australia. Besides New Zealand, Persoonias are restricted to Australia.

*Persoonia stricta*

# Petrophile

From the Greek 'petra' a rock and 'philos' beloved, so is a "lover of rocks", which the early botanist Robert Brown presumed was their preferred habitat. Here in the west nearly all the species prefer sandy or gravelly soils. The conical flowering heads have led to the common name 'Coneflower'. There are 39 species in Australia and 33 of these are in the west.

Petrophile are low to medium woody shrubs and the flowers occur in dense spikes or cones. The genus is closely linked with Isopogon but differs in having persistent woody cone bracts.

*Petrophile biloba* Granite Petrophile

# Xylomelum
## Woody Pear

From the Greek xylon-wood and melon-tree fruit, referring to the hard woody fruits.

As the fruits of all species are large woody and rather like inverted pears, they are know as woody pears. There are 5 species with just two in the south west. The flowering tree is quite spectacular but most people do not see them as they are in full bloom in the height of our hot summer, January to February.

*Petrophile longifolia* Long-leaved Cone Bush

*Xylomelum angustifolium* Woody Pear

*Petrophile linearis* Pixie Mops

*Eucalyptus erythrocorys* Illyarrie  *Darwinia oxylepis* Gillams Bell  *Melaleuca diosmifolia*

# Myrtaceae
## Myrtle family—Eucalypts, Bottlebrushes & Tea trees

A very large family predominantly found in the southern hemisphere including south east Asia. About 75, half of the genera arenative to Australia. There are approximately 1500 species with over half being found in Western Australia.

The Family name is derived from the Mediterranean genus Myrtus (myrtle).

Myrtaceae is divided into two sub families Leptospermoideae with dry capsular fruits and almost solely restricted to Australia, and Myrtoideae with succulent fruits mainly found in South America.

# Callistemon
## *Bottlebrushes*

This genus of red flowers is more common in eastern Australia, only 2 species occuring in WA. The stamens are free.

*Beaufortia sparsa* Swamp Bottlebrush

*Beaufortia orbifolia* Ravensthorpe Bottlebrush

*Beaufortia incana*

# Calothamnus

## One Sided Bottlebrush or Clawflower

This genus is about 40 species noted for its bright red flowers and is restricted to Western Australia. The genus is cultivated throughout the world.

*Calothamnus sanquineus* Bindak

*Calothamnus pinifolius* Dense Clawflower

# Verticordia
## Featherflowers

*Verticordia mitchelliana*
Rapier Featherflower

Almost totally restricted to Western Australia. The genus supports a fantastic range of variously coloured species and in some areas is the dominant flower when in bloom, particularly late November and early December. The feathery calyx lobes are the feature of this genus.

*Verticordia monadelpha* Pink Woolly Featherflower

*Verticordia noblis*

*Verticordia mulleriana*

# Eucalyptus
## Eucalypts or Gum Trees

If one thinks of Australia and its plants, Eucalypts are perhaps the first thing that comes to mind. They can be found through out Australia from the cold snow capped mountains to the edge of rainforests and in our desert regions.

Eucalyptus is the largest genus in the family Myrtaceae with over 600 species with more than half occuring in Western Australia. The greatest number occur in the semi arid woodlands of the south west.

The name Eucalyptus was proposed by the French botanist L'Heritier working at the British museum. It comes from the Greek 'eu' meaning well and 'calyptos' meaning covered, in reference to the hard cap that covers the emerging flowers prior to them blooming. The cap protects the reproductive parts of the flower from the intense heat of the sun until the stamens are fully advanced and ready to expand and bloom.

*Eucalyptus caesia* Gungurru

*Eucalyptus grossa* Coarse-leaved Mallee

*Eucalyptus tetraptera* Four-winged Mallee

*Eucalyptus accedens* Powderbark Wandoo

*Eucalyptus lehmanni* Bushy Yate

# Melaleuca
## Paperbark & Honey Myrtle

The genus Melaleuca is predominantly an Australian genus being found through the country with over 200 species and only 10 species outside Australia. There are over 120 species in WA.

Many of the larger Melaleucas are called paperbarks due to the papery quality of the bark and most are found near water. The desert Aborigines were well aware of this fact when looking for water.

*Melaleuca diosmifolia*

*Melaleuca cuticularis* Water Paperbark

# Chamelaucium
## Waxflowers

There are just over 10 species in this genus and the Geraldton Wax Chamelaucium uncinatum is a very popular horticultural plant, especially in the cut flower trade.

*Chamelaucium megalopetalum* Esperance Waxflower

# Pileanthus
## Coppercups

*Pileanthus filifolius*
Summer Coppercups

There are just 3 species in this genus but they certainly bring a wonderful splash of colour to the heaths of the south west with their bright pink and orange flowers.

*Pileanthus peduncularis* Coppercups

# Scholtzia

*Scholtzia uberiflora*

# Kunzea

*Kunzea ericifolia* Spearwood

# Darwinea
## Native Bells

*Darwinia citriodora* Lemon-scented Darwinia

The genus is named after Erasmus Darwin, grandfather of the naturalist Charles Darwin. There are 32 species in the south west and it is in the Stirling Range National Park that some of the most spectacular bells can be found, with individual species restricted to separate peaks.

*Darwinia meeboldii* Cranbrook Bell

*Darwinia oxylepis* Gillams Bell

# Calytrix
## *Star Flowers*

There are just over 30 species in this genus and they come in many colours.

*Calytrix decandra* Pink Star Flower

*Calytrix brevifolia* A Star Flower

# eptospermum
## *Tea Trees*

*Leptospermum sericeum*

# Hypocalymma
## *Myrtles*

*Hypocalymma angustrfolium* White Myrtle

Restricted to the south west. Many of the species have bright pink flowers and make a wonderful show in the Jarrah and Marri forest as well as the Banksia Eucalypt woodland near Perth.

# Orchidaceae
## Orchid family

This is one of the largest plant families in the world with over 700 genera and a staggering 25,000 species. In Australia alone there is over 900 species. Orchids comprise two main groups, the epiphytes that grow above ground on their host tree and terrestrial orchids that grow in the ground. Over half of the Australian orchids are epiphytes but interestingly, in the south west all 300 orchid species are terrestrial. One particular orchid in the south west grows entirely underground while the Hammer orchid of the genus Drakea, resembles a wingless female wasp. The male wasp of this species attempts to pick up the wingless "female" and in doing so, brushes its body against the pollen on the labellum. When the male wasp visits any other hammer orchids the pollen is deposited on the stigma and cross pollination occurs. But the story does not end there. To attract the male wasp, in addition to the shape, the Hammer orchid has a chemical scent to that of the real female wasp, making it more enticing to visit.

*Caladenia falcata* Green Spider Orchid

*Thelymitra villosa*
Custard Orchid

*Thelyn*

*panulata* Shirt Orchid    *Caladenia varians subsp. noblis* Noble Spider Orchid    *Diurius corymbosa* Common Donkey Orchid

*Swainsonia formosa*
Sturt Pea

# Fabaceae
## Pea family

Leguminous plants (pod and bean bearers) constitute one of the largest and most economically important plant families in the world as they provide many of the plants we eat such as the garden pea Pisum sativum and the broad bean Vicia faba, the soya bean Glycine max and the peanut Arachis hypogea. World wide there are about 500 genera with 12,000 species. Australia has about 140 genera and 1100 species and WA has well over half, about 650 species.

The family name is derived from the genus Faba which is the latin word for bean. The majority of the pea family contain nitrogen-fixing bacteria and these convert atmospheric nitrogen into nitrogenous compounds that the plants utilize.

**Swainsonia**

# Urodon

*Urodon dasyphylla* Mop Bushpea

A small genus with only two species found here in WA.

# Kennedia

*Kennedia prostrata* Running Postman

Is endemic to Australia with 16 species of which 12 are found in the south west.

# Jacksonia

*Jacksonia floribunda* Holly Pea

In WA there are over 40 species in this genus and many of them are leafless. Their flowers are predominantly yellow to orange and red.

# Chorizema *Flame peas*

*Chorizema dicksonii* Yellow-eyed Flame Pea

This genus is called flame peas due to their brilliant colours. There are 25 species in Australia with all but one occuring in WA.

# Gastrolobium
*poison peas*

*Gastrolobium bilobum* Heart leaved Poison

Another large genus in the pea family with over 50 species in Australia and most of these in WA. All are poisonous to stock and some species are now very rare due to intense eradication programs in the early settlement days. The constituents in the poison are very similar to the poison 1080 and this has been used successfully in baiting meat to eradicate the European fox, as the native fauna are immune to the toxins in this poison.

# Hovea

*Hovea stricta*

Of the 20 species in this genus WA has eight. All are purple or blue in colour and make a wonderful contrast with the beautiful yellows of the Karri wattle in the deep south west.

# Nemcia

*Nemcia rubra* Mountain Pea
There are 28 species in or orange, occasionally

...stly with yellow
...vers.

## Daviesia
### Bitter pea or Rattle pod

*Daviesia incrassata*
This is a large genus with over 90 species in WA alone. Many of the species are very prickly with no leaves, and develop a triangular seed pod that rattles when the seed is well developed, hence its common name.

## Gompholobium

*Gompholobrium polymorphan*
There are just over 40 species, all but one being endemic to Australia and the majority being found in the south west. The name is derived from the Greek gomphos meaning club and lobas meaning pod.

## Crotalaria
### Rattle Pod

*Crotalaria novae-hollandiae* New Holland Rattlepod
The name is derived from the Greek cratalon meaning to rattle, hence the seeds rattle inside the pod when shaken. There are 18 species in WA mostly found in the tropical region.

# Mimosaceae
## Mimosa family, wattles (Acacia)

The family is widespread throughout the tropics and sub tropics and warm temperate regions of the world. Of the 17 Australian genera, the largest by far is the genus Acacia with over 900 species and over 400 being found in the west. Australian Aborigines used the seeds for food, and the timber for implements such as spears and boomerangs. The flowers are mostly bright yellow, occasionally cream or white, and resemble fluffy balls or spikes. The leaf structure varies immensely from soft dissected leaves to simple hard spiky leaflike structures which make them a fascinating plant group to study.

*Acacia acuminata* Rasberry Jam

*Acacia glaucoptera* Flat-leaved Wattle

*Acacia wildenowiana* Grass Wattle

# Haemodoraceae
## Kangaroo paw family

The family is predominantly a southern hemisphere family with 14 genera and 103 species. All contain interesting chemicals that have been used for colouring dyes.

The genus Anigozanthos Kangaroo paws has 12 species in WA with the addition of several sub species. The Red and Green Kangaroo paw *Anigozanthos manglesii*, is Western Australia's floral emblem and is used extensively in the wildflower trade. Conostylis is the largest genus in the Haemodoraceae family with 46 species, all confined to WA.

*Anigozanthus viridis* Green Kangaroo Paw

*Anigozanthus manglessii* Mangle's Kangaroo Paw

*Anigozanthus rufus* Red Kangaroo Paw

*Macropidia fuliginosa* Black Kangaroo Paw

*Anigozanthus humilis sub.sp grandis* Giant Catspaw

# Amaranthaceae
## *Amaranth family*

A large family found in the tropics and sub tropics of the world, especially the Americas, Africa and Australia. In WA the plants that are indigenous to this state are Ptilotus (Mulla Mulla) and Gomphrena. They are mainly found in the drier regions of the state and rely on the autumn and winter rains to bring them to life. Together with the everlastings they form wonderful carpets of colour, especially in the Mulga region after good rains.

*Ptilotus manglesii* Pom Poms

*Ptilotus macrocephalus* Featherheads

*Ptilotus exaltatus* Tall Mulla Mulla

# Asteraceae
## Daisy family

The daisy family is distributed throughout the world and is one of the largest flowering plant families with over 200 genera and well over 25,000 species. In WA there are just over 450 species.

They are considered advanced in evolutionary terms and are certainly one of the most successful plant groups, having adapted to almost every ecological niche.

An important family characteristic is that each flower head is comprised of many tiny individual flowers, encircled by brightly coloured rays (bracts)

Everlastings is a general term for some of the species that have a dry papery flower structure, retaining their colour for many years after they have been picked.

*Waitzia suaveolens* Fragrant Waitzia

*Brachyscome iberidifolia* Native Daisy

*Lawrencella davenportii* Sticky everlasting

# Apiaceae
## Carrot, parsley & fennel family

# Dilleniaceae
## Guinea flowers & Hibbertia

*Xanthosia rotundifolia* Southern Cross

A large family of herbs often with characteristic odours. Southern Cross, Xanthosia rotundifolia is an easily recognized flower in our south west forests.

*Hibbertia cuneformus* Cutleaf Hibbertia

The majority of the plants in this group are restricted to the tropical and subtropical regions of the world and the genus. Hibbertia is widespread throughout southern Australia. The bright yellow flowers with two lobed petals are very conspicuous in the spring.

# Cupressaceae
## Native Pines

A world wide family with 9 species being found in WA.

*Callitris glaucophylla* White Cypress Pine

# Chloanthaceae
## Native foxglove, lambswool & lambs tails

This family is restricted to Australia and all 10 general and most of the 104 species can be found in WA mainly in the drier regions of the state.

*Lachnostachys ferruginea*
Rusty Lambstail

*Pityrodia atriplicina* A Foxglove

# Epacridaceae
## Heath family

Again a predominantly Australian family but some genera are found in south east Asia, New Zealand and the Pacific Islands. There are approx. 430 species in Australia. The Epacridaceae have been called heaths as they resemble the heaths and heathers of Europe, but are a totally different family. Most of the Epacridacea are small woody plants with small tough tubular flowers and pointed leaves.

*Andersonia caerulea* Foxtails

*Astroloma foliosum* Crandle Cranberry

*Astroloma cilatum* Moss leaved he

*Astroloma stomarrhena* Red Swamp Cranberry

*Leucopogon verticillatus* Tassel Flower

# Droseraceae
## Sundews

These are insectivorous plants and are recognized by their leaves which are covered with sticky, sensitive, staked glands. Flies and other small insects are trapped in these sticky glands. After digestion by the enzymes in the sticky glands, the body contents are absorbed by the plant, the glands return to the normal position and the insect skeleton falls to the ground. This adds additional nutriment to the plant. Many of the species grow from a tuberous structure underground and lie dormant until the first winter rains stimulate growth.

The name is taken from the Greek 'droseros' meaning dewy, as the fluids exuded by the plant look like dewy droplets in the rising or setting suns rays.

There are about 46 species in WA.

*Drosera menziesii* Pink Rainbow

*Drosera stolonifera* Leafy Sundew

# Liliaceae
## *Lillies*

This is a cosmopolitan family with over 4000 species and in WA there are over 200 species. Thysanotus the genus illustrated below is the largest, with over 50 species and most of them in WA. The name is derived from the Greek thysanotos meaning fringe, hence the common name Fringed Lily.

*Thysanotus dichotomus* Branching Fringe Lily

*Thysanotus patersonii* Twining Fringe Lily

*Drosera erythrorhiza* Red Ink Sundew

# Goodeniaceae
## Goodenias, Leschenaultias

A large family with 17 genera found in Australia. The WA genus Lechenaultia is the most widely cultivated member of the family and there is more colour variation with in the genus than most other plants, having blue, violet, yellow, orange, red and green flowers. One species that is of particular interest is the Wreath Leschenaultia, Leschenaultia macrantha, found in the Mullewa region. It's flowers grow on the outer perimeter of the circular shaped plant.

The genus Goodenia has also some very attractive flowers with over 50 species ocurring in WA. The genus Dampiera is named after William Dampier who made the first collection of pressed plants from WA. In WA these species are mostly blue to violet in colour. The quantity of blue species astounded the early botanist as the colour blue is not a common colour in the plant world. There are 36 species of Dampiera in WA.

*Scaevola calliptera* Royal Robe

*Goodenia dyeri*

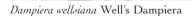

*Dampiera wellsiana* Well's Dampiera

*Lechenaultia macrantha* Wreath Lechenaultia

*Lechenaultia formosa* Red Lechenaultia

*Lechenaultia acutiloba* Wingless Lechenaultia

*Lechenaultia tubiflora* Heath Lechenaultia

# Loranthaceae
## Mistletoe family

The majority of mistletoes are parasitic, that is they derive nourishment from the host plant, and grow on the branches of their host tree. Most produce a sticky rich glucose covered seed which is eaten by the Mistletoe bird. It is their major food source. The seed is digested in 4 to 10 minutes and then defecated on the host tree, dropping the still sticky seed on another branch, thus ensuring the propagation of the mistletoe. There are over 20 species of mistletoe in WA but its single European relative Viscum album does not exist here.

An exception to the other common mistletoes is the Christmas Tree Nuytsia floribunda The Christmas tree is an independent plant, gaining some of its nourishment from the roots of other plants and the species name certainly describes it well, as the bright orange flowers set against the clear summer blue skies in December and January are quite a sight to behold.

*Nuytsia floribunda* Christmas Tree

# Malvaceae
## Mallow family

Hibiscus is the largest genus of the mallow family, comprising over 300 species world wide with 24 in WA. A distinctive feature of the family is that the stamens are united to form a tubular column in the centre of each flower.

*Alyogyne Hakeaefolia* Red-centred Hibiscus

# Myporaceae
## Emu or Poverty Bush

Quite a large genus with over 125 species occuring in Western Australia. Most are found in the drier regions of the state and are a major source of nectar for desert frequenting birds such as Black, Pied, Grey and Spiney cheeked Honeyeaters.

*Eremophila forrestii* Wilcox Bush

*Eremophila fraseri* Turpentine Bush

The name is derived from the genus Ruta. The family is widespread in the tropics and sub tropics especially South America, Australia and South Africa. In Australia there is a total of 41 genera and 320 species. Many species are scented due to the presence of oil glands in their leaves and flowers. Some boronias are grown solely for their use in perfumes.

*Diplolaena grandiflora* Tamala Rose

*Nemiataleps phebalioides*

*Boronia cymosa* Granite Boronia

## Polygalaceae
### Milkworts

A world wide family in the genus Comesperma, having the most species in Australia.

## Santaceae
### Sandalwood

All sandalwoods are semi-parasitic, deriving some nourishment from roots of other plants by means of sucker type root attachments. The quandong Santalum acuminatum has bright red fruits which are used to make a sweet jam, and its relative Sandalwood Santalum spicatum, is still cut for the incense trade and used for joss sticks in east Asia.

## Sapindacae
### Hop bushes

This is a worldwide family and Dodonaea illustrated here is the largest Australian genus with over 30 species in WA.

*Comesperma confertum* Milkwort

*Santalum murrayanum* Bitter Quandong

*Dodonaea stenozyga* Native Hop

# Stackhousiaceae
## Stackhousia

There are only 3 genera in this family which is almost entirely restricted to Australia. The largest genus is Stackhousia, with fragrant flowers particularly noticeable at night and which are pollinated by moths.

Eriostemon spicatus *Pepper & Salt*

*Stackhousia monogyna* A Stackhousia

# Sterculiaceae
## Kurrajongs & paper flowers

Largely tropical to sub tropical family world wide. The Kurrajongs mostly found in the north of Australia store water which the Aborigines used to tap in drought. In the south west these species are mainly low herbs with the showy calyx being the visible part of the flower.

*Keraudrena integrifolia* Common Firebush

# Thymelaeacae
## Daphne family—Riceflowers

This is a small family group found in the temperate and tropical regions of the world. The family derives its name from the genus Melaea, a native of Asia and the Mediterranean. The main genus in WA is Pimelea commonly Riceflowers, with about 37 species.

*Pimelea ciliata* White Banjine

*Pimelea physodes (red flowered form)* Qualup Bell

*Pimelea squaveolens* Scented Banjine

# Xanthorroeaceae
## Grass Trees & Matt Rush

Of the 9 genera of Xanthorroeaceae only one extends outside Australia. For most species, flowering is stimulated by fire. The Grass trees were very useful to the Aborigines who ate the young shoots and the resins from the leaf base was used as an adhesive.

*Dasypogon hookeri* Pineapple Bush

*Xanthorrhoea pressii* Grass Tree

*Xanthorrhoea gracilis* Dwarf Grass Tree

# Index of Scientific Names Families are in capitals and bold print.

# Index of Common Names

Simon Nevill

Simon has taken on many occupations through his life. Being a qualified furniture designer he spent much of his life in the interior and furniture design world but his real love and passion has been the study of natural history and the protection of the environment. Having led birdwatching tours worldwide for over fourteen years now, Simon is concentrating on producing books to bring his love of the outdoors to all.